פסוקה

ArtScroll Youth Series®

Rabbi Nosson Scherman / Rabbi Meir Zlotowitz
General Editors

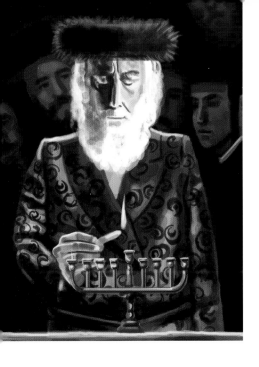

Touched by a Story 2

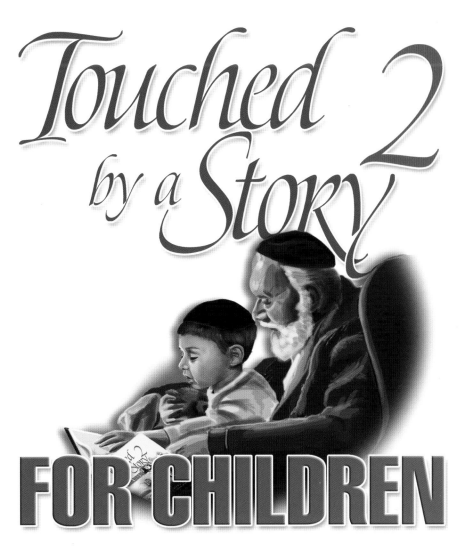

FOR CHILDREN

RABBI YECHIEL SPERO
ILLUSTRATED BY SHAYA SCHONFELD

Published by

Mesorah Publications, ltd

ARTSCROLL YOUTH SERIES®

"TOUCHED BY A STORY FOR CHILDREN 2"

© *Copyright 2007 by* Mesorah Publications, Ltd.
First edition – First impression: June, 2007

Published by **MESORAH PUBLICATIONS, LTD.**
4401 Second Avenue / Brooklyn, N.Y 11232 / (718) 921-9000 / Fax: (718) 680-1875
www.artscroll.com

Distributed in Israel by SIFRIATI / A. GITLER — BOOKS
6 Hayarkon Street / Bnei Brak 51127

Distributed in Europe by LEHMANNS
Unit E, Viking Business Park, Rolling Mill Road / Jarrow, Tyne and Wear / England NE32 3DP

Distributed in Australia and New Zealand by GOLD'S WORLD OF JUDAICA
3-13 William Street / Balaclava, Melbourne 3183, Victoria, Australia

Distributed in South Africa by KOLLEL BOOKSHOP
Ivy Common, 105 William Road / Norwood 2192 / Johannesburg, South Africa

Printed in the USA by Noble Book Press Corp.
Custom bound by Sefercraft, Inc. / 4401 Second Avenue / Brooklyn N.Y. 11232

ISBN 10: 1-4226-0549-3
ISBN 13: 978-1-4226-0549-3

Contents

My One and Only Mitzvah

av Binyamin Diskin was a well-known *gadol* who lived in the town of Brisk. He was known far and wide for his greatness in learning. He was also always careful to do mitzvos properly.

During the entire year he was careful about which foods he ate, where he walked, and to whom he spoke. Before Rosh Hashanah and Yom Kippur he was even more careful. People in Brisk, like in most places, were very nervous before Rosh Hashanah and Yom Kippur, knowing that the days of judgment were coming near. Reb Binyomin was also known for being extra careful in his *davening* during these days. He would *daven* so sincerely, knowing how much was at stake.

One year as the *shul* filled for *Kol Nidrei,* the Rav's seat remained empty. Murmuring began among those who had already gathered — normally Reb Binyamin was early for this important event. The sun started setting and more and more people filled the room. The entire *shul* was practically full, but still there was no sign of Reb Binyamin. Some wondered if he was feeling well, even though that would usually not have stopped him from coming to *daven* on *Kol Nidrei* night.

Another fifteen minutes went by and by now everyone was whispering, "Where is Reb Binyamin? What could he possibly be doing that is more important than *davening* on Yom Kippur?" They started wondering if perhaps something had happened to their Rav.

Search teams were sent out to cover the town and look for the Rav. They carefully searched the roads he might have passed through, but he was nowhere to be found. They finally made their way back to his home and knocked on the door, afraid of what they might find. At first they heard nothing and braced themselves for the worst. But then, as they were about to force their way into his home, they heard voices inside.

Again they knocked, but this time with a little more force. "Rebbi, are you hurt? Is everything all right?"

Suddenly the door opened and before them stood Rav Binyamin dressed in his white *kitel*. He looked at them and then looked back at the wooden table in his house. At the table sat his son Yehoshua Leib, with two large volumes

of *Gemara* open in front of him. Rav Binyamin had apparently just been learning with his son. The Rav invited the men to enter and tell him why they had come.

The members of the congregation explained that they were worried, since the hour was late and the Rav had not yet come to *shul*. Rav Binyamin looked at the dark sky outside. It was long past sunset, the time when *Kol Nidrei* is normally said. He then looked back at the men and explained. "You know that tonight is Yom Kippur. It is the day when our mitzvos and *aveiros* are weighed. And I began thinking about how I could spend the last moments before this awesome day. There are not many mitzvos that I perform properly but there is one that I know I fulfill correctly, and that is the mitzvah of *veshinantam levanecha* – learning Torah with my son."

The stunned men realized that, in fact, everything was fine in the Diskin home. The silence lasted for a long moment.

"*Rabbosai*, I beg you. I need all the *zechusim* I can get. Please don't take away the one mitzvah that I do correctly."

Slowly the men walked back toward the door through which they had entered. What they had just seen was truly incredible. To Rav Binyamin the one thing that mattered most was learning Torah with his son, and he would allow nothing to stop him from doing that. True, the *kehillah* was waiting, but he was simply unable to pull himself away. A moment passed and they could not keep the *shul* waiting any longer. Rav Binyomin closed the *Gemaras* and walked to *shul* with his beloved son, Yehoshua Leib, who would one day grow up to be the Rav of Yerushalayim.

The Great Linen Robbery

No one could figure it out. Who would dare think of stealing from the Rebbe of Rudnick, Rabbi Yekusiel Yehudah Halberstam? After all, he was such a gracious, kind, and caring person. Nevertheless, the previous evening, at around 7 o'clock, the rebbetzin had come running into her husband's study. The unthinkable had happened. Someone had broken into their home and stolen their entire set of linens. The pillows, blankets, and sheets had been taken directly off their beds! The rebbetzin was shocked! Who would dare break into the Rebbe's home and steal his belongings? Didn't these people have shame? And what was most surprising was that the Rebbe's followers had not noticed anything unusual. The Rebbe reassured his rebbetzin that everything Hashem did was for the best. He suggested that they forget about it. He was afraid that word would spread throughout the town, and the townspeople would overreact. But the mystery of the missing linen remained unsolved. No one seemed to have any answers ....

The woman tapped lightly on the door. She knew that the Rebbe was not receiving visitors but she felt that she had no choice but to disturb him. The door opened and the Rebbe greeted the woman as if he had been expecting her. "Rebbe," she cried out. "Mazel Tov! My daughter's a *kallah*!" At first, the Rebbe reacted with joy, but then he saw that the mother was crying. When he asked, she explained that although she was very thankful that her daughter had finally become a *kallah,* she was ashamed that she had nothing to give to the couple. Normally, a *chasan* was given a *nadan*, money for the couple to begin their lives together, and they also received dishes, pots, and many more

items to help them set up their home. But she was a widow. Not only couldn't she provide the standard *nadan*, but she could not come up with the money for any of the other basic needs either. She could not afford to buy dishes, tablecloths, furniture — nothing. She was embarrassed for herself and for her daughter. So she was turning to the kindest person she knew — the Rebbe of Rudnick.

The Rebbe listened to her words and understood her difficulty. Even though she tried to stop crying, the love she felt for her daughter and her desire to give was so strong that the woman could not be calmed. After much thought, the Rebbe decided on a plan and told her to come back at 6 o'clock that evening, but to use the side entrance of the house.

Shmuel Greenbaum, one of the Rebbe's close followers before the Second World War, was walking down the street on his way to the local *shtiebel* when he noticed something strange. Someone, although he had no idea who, had parked a wagon on the street outside the Rebbe's house. It looked like linen was being stolen from the Rebbe's house! Shmuel quickly ran up to the door to stop the thief, but when he grabbed the man he was shocked to find that it was the Rebbe himself!

"Rebbe, I'm so sorry! I thought …"

The Rebbe turned toward Shmuel and spoke to him in a firm manner. "I ask you to please keep what you are now seeing to yourself." Shmuel asked the Rebbe what was happening and whether he could help out. The Rebbe led Shmuel into his room and asked him to help strip the linen from his bed and fold it up so it could be put into the wagon. The Rebbi told him that it was for a *Yiddishe meidel,* a *kallah*. Shmuel was ordered never to tell the secret of the missing linens, as long as the Rebbi was alive.

Indeed, until the day the Rebbe left this world, no one ever solved the mystery of the "Great Linen Robbery."

You Get What You Deserve

av Shabsi Frankel proudly showed the Steipler Gaon his new edition of the Rambam. He and so many others had worked so hard on it for many years. Upon seeing it, the Steipler smiled and said, "The Rambam and his commentators will wait to greet you in Gan Eden!"

Reb Shabsi and the scholars working with him had gathered and studied hundreds of different texts that would help to improve the truth and quality of the printed editions of the Rambam. The manuscripts were worth millions of dollars and had taken many years to acquire. One incident that occurred during this time shows that Reb Shabsi was much more than a Torah scholar.

One day, Reb Shabsi and another respected *talmid chacham* were working together on one of the rare manuscripts at Reb Shabsi's home. For hours on end they worked, studying the ancient pages and comparing them to each other. This needed endless patience. Reb Shabsi's wife saw how hard the men were working and brought them two cups of coffee. His back to the kitchen, the other scholar did not notice the coffee being brought in, and accidentally spilled his coffee on the priceless manuscript when the cup was placed on the table!

Reb Shabsi jumped up and ran into the kitchen. He most certainly was upset that his valuable manuscript was ruined, but he did not want to embarrass the man in any way. Two minutes later he came out of the kitchen with a fresh cup of coffee. "I figured since the first one spilled you would probably want another one."

The man smiled. He knew that what had happened had probably caused Reb Shabsi to be disappointed and upset, but he also knew that Reb Shabsi understood it was an accident that could happen to anyone. The Stzeipler's comment about the Rambam being eager to greet Reb Shabsi had never seemed truer.

"The Rambam and his commentators will wait to greet you in Gan Eden!" But maybe not because of the reason we had originally thought.

Making Him Happy

here was so much excitement in the air. It was visiting day in Camp Machaneinu — time for parents, family, and friends to visit the campers. The evening before, the camp's head counselor, Rabbi Cukier, had spoken about the importance of making sure that all bunkhouses were clean and that each and every boy had showered the night before and was dressed nicely. He also stressed that it was very important that when the parents arrived, they not be greeted by anxious, greedy children who just wanted to see what their parents had brought for them. Rather, he stressed the opportunity to finally be able to show the proper *kibud av va'eim,* a mitzvah that they had not been able to perform over the past few weeks because they were not at home.

The next morning the boys woke up earlier than usual. Each boy put on his nicest outfit and most washed up carefully, as Rabbi Cukier had instructed. Although learning groups were officially over at 10:15, the parents began to trickle onto the campus even before then, anxious to sneak a peek at their child's learning group.

The kids in the learning groups struggled not to become too distracted by the parents who were peering into the rooms. The broadcast, "Time for learning never ends, but learning groups are now over," was announced over the loudspeaker and before long a buzz was in the air. Hundreds of parents were reunited with their children, and younger siblings watched in awe as their brothers showed them around the beautiful campus. They proudly showed off all of the camp's attractions — the new gym and go-kart track as well as the neat little pocket rockets that had become so popular. Also on the tour was the *shul* where each child pointed out the chart that showed points earned for learning.

With all this excitement, it was easy to miss the little boy all alone in the parking lot. Shmuli Lipmanowitz just sat there on the large white rock at the boundary of the lot. "Are your parents coming today, Shmuli?" Rabbi Cukier called out. He knew that Shmuli had been expecting them, but perhaps there had been some sort of change.

"Yeah! They sure are! I'm sure they'll be here soon. They probably just got stuck in traffic."

Shmuli was not one of the more popular kids in camp. In fact, he had few friends and was very much a loner. The kids in his bunk knew this well and did their best to include him in all the goings-on, but more often than

not Shmuli ended up wandering around camp, looking for things to do. He seemed so lonely then! Sometimes Rabbi Cukier would ask him to help in the camp office with some small tasks, but Shmuli would quickly become sad and go back to his bunk.

Today, though, something seemed more sad than usual about Shmuli's loneliness. As the cars continued to pile in and pull out, filled with children laughing and smiling, Shmuli became sadder and sadder. Rabbi Cukier came by every 15 minutes or so and invited Shmuli back to his own bungalow, but he was always met with the same response, "Nah, it's okay. I'm going to wait here for my parents .... They're going to be coming soon."

The scene broke Rabbi Cukier's heart. He could not imagine anything sadder. But even when he offered to take the boy bowling or to the pizza shop, Shmuli refused. He still had hope his parents would come. As the day wore on, though, Shmuli's spirits began to sink and finally, with his head bowed, he went back to his bunk.

A few minutes later Rabbi Cukier decided to check on him and peeked through the bunkhouse window. His heart nearly broke as he watched the boy sobbing bitterly into his pillow. He wanted to go in and cheer him up, but he knew that there was really nothing more to say. Shmuli's parents had let him down and he was utterly devastated. After all, who could blame him?

After two hours of continuously checking on Shmuli, Rabbi Cukier walked past the bunkhouse and noticed that the bed was empty. In a way Rabbi Cukier was relieved. Perhaps the boy had overcome his disappointment, at least for the moment. But then Rabbi Cukier saw something that was very upsetting — it looked as though another boy was stealing something from under Shmuli's pillow! Unable to control his disappointment, he rushed into the bunkhouse and asked the youngster what he was trying to do. "Why are you taking something from underneath Shmuli's pillow?"

The question was more of an accusation than a question. The young boy, Avromi Shleifer, stammered his way through the embarrassing situation. "I ... um ... was ... um ... not stealing anything ... um ... from under his pillow."

"Really?! Then what *were* you doing?"

Avromi looked away as he turned red. Rabbi Cukier normally would have allowed the boy a way out with a just a lecture. But Shmuli had just made

it through one of the most disappointing days he would ever have. And having something stolen on top of that was just too much for one little boy to handle.

Finally Avromi looked up. He had tears in his eyes and could barely get the words out. He knew what he was being accused of. "Really, I didn't steal anything from Shmuli ... I was just ...."

"You were just what?!" By now Rabbi Cukier was extremely upset.

He grabbed the package out of Avromi's hand and stared at it. On the package was written, *"For Shmuli ... Sorry we couldn't make it today ... We love you. Mommy and Daddy."*

But, surprisingly, the writing was very childish, as if it were written by ... a 10-year-old.

And then Rabbi Cukier realized what had happened. Avromi held his head down. Rabbi Cukier placed his hand on Avromi's chin and lifted his head up. "Avromi, tell me the truth."

"Well ... I was in my parents' car when I saw Shmuli standing on the side of the road. And later when I came back he was still there. I realized that his parents must not have come to visit him so I made a package for him. And I signed a note from his parents.

"I'm sorry ... I thought it would make him happy ...."

Avromi held his head down and Rabbi Cukier wiped the tears from his own eyes. He had never witnessed such selfless and thoughtful behavior from anyone, let alone a 10-year-old boy. He placed the package back under Shmuli's pillow and put his arm around Avromi's shoulder.

"You will make him happy, Avromi, I'm sure of it ..."

And one can only imagine how happy he made his Father in Heaven.

Well Worth It

It was a very cold European winter, and Dovid bundled up as well as he could and ran outside. Though only 8 years old, he was already careful enough to be worried that he was going to be late for school, so he ran, ignoring the biting wind. He wanted to be on time in order to learn as much as possible, for he truly loved learning. Together with a number of other boys, he was taught Torah by a local *melamed.* Such was the schedule for many children in the mid-1750's in Europe.

Many families at that time were very, very poor. Dovid and his family suffered more than most, however. His father worked hard just to put bread and a few basic foods on the table. They did not have the money to buy new shoes or sweaters or pants. But one year Dovid developed a bad cold that just did not get better, so his parents decided to do what they knew they must — buy a warm winter coat for him.

Dovid waited anxiously for his new coat. He could not remember the last time he had worn something that was not used, and when he finally went to the tailor to pick up the new coat he was overjoyed. But it had come at a price — and a costly one at that. For several months, instead of the little food that Dovid and his family usually managed to survive on, they had to make do with even less, cutting back on "luxuries" like butter and beans. But it was worth it to them, especially if it meant that Dovid would be able to learn better.

Young Dovid wore his new coat proudly and was very thankful that his father had worked so hard and saved to pay for it. So the next day he dashed out of the house, eager to show his new coat to all his friends, and ran all the way to the *cheder*. The cold wind brought the temperature down to well below zero, and the other boys in the group also came in all bundled up against the cold.

Shimon, the oldest boy in the class, walked in with two scarves around his head and neck; and Eliezer, one of Dovid's closest friends, was wearing fairly new boots that kept his feet warm and dry. Reuven had a new hat that his *bubby* had knitted for him, and now Dovid could include himself in that group. How good it felt to finally be able to walk into the room and not take so long to warm up from the freezing cold!

As the *shiur* began they realized that one boy was going to be late today — Avromi. Then again, Avromi was late every day. Avromi was the youngest in the group. He was a year younger than Dovid and wore a shirt that was

too big and pants that were torn. He never complained, although his shoes allowed the cold rain and snow to seep through. It was almost as if his feet never warmed up.

Avromi entered the room with his lips trembling and his teeth chattering, and Dovid could not help but be distracted by Avromi's terrible discomfort. The *shiur* finished and then it was time to return home. Upon opening the door of the room, they were reminded of the freezing weather they were about to go out into once again.

Dovid, bundled and warm, looked at the torn jacket little Avromi was wearing. As Dovid was about to walk out the door he stopped suddenly, unbuttoned his brand-new coat and placed it onto a surprised Avromi. At first Avromi did not know how to react. But then his smile grew wide — in fact, he could hardly stop smiling. He thanked Dovid for the coat and ran out the door to embrace the weather he had dreaded just a few minutes earlier.

Dovid put on Avromi's tattered coat and ran through the streets until he finally arrived at his door. As he burst into the house and shut the door against the howling wind, his mother took one look at him and said, "Dovid, where's your brand-new coat?"

Dovid apologized as he mumbled something about giving it to his younger friend, Avromi. "I'm sorry, I just couldn't watch him walk outside with his torn jacket. I'll go back to wearing my old coat …."

His mother, although quite proud of her son's kindness, was shocked and at a loss for words. "But what will your father say? You know that he saved up for a long time for that coat. When he finds out what you did he may punish you …."

Dovid thought for a moment. He thought of Avromi's face each and every morning as he arrived at the *shiur*. He looked so cold and uncomfortable. And then Dovid simply declared, "That's fine. It's worth it. If it means that Avromi will be warm, then I don't mind being punished."

His father came home. Although he was disappointed, he had come to expect this type of kindness from his son. He knew that his son was extremely caring, that he had a very special *neshamah*. And young Dovid grew up to become the great Rav Dovid Lelover, the Lelover Rebbe — a man who warmed the hearts of thousands.

A Simple Menorah

The Divrei Chaim always said that no one should be ashamed of his past behavior. He once revealed that when he was young, he was such a miser that when his mother gave him a piece of cake to bring to *cheder* he would sell the crumbs to his friends. But he overcame his stinginess as he got older – in fact, he became so generous that he would give away his own valuables, even precious family treasures that had been passed down from previous generations. It is told that on three separate occasions he even gave his own menorah to poor people so that they could sell it back to him! One such story happened one year on the day before Chanukah.

The glorious silver menorah was being polished in honor of Chanukah, but when it came time to light it, the menorah was nowhere to be found. The family members looked all over for it. Soon they began to worry that someone had had the chutzpah to steal the Rebbe's menorah. Suddenly Reb Chaim appeared, wanting to know what all the commotion was about. They broke the news to him that the menorah was missing and was possibly stolen. But Reb Chaim wasn't worried in the least — he explained that a poor person had come to the door and he had given him the menorah. His family was shocked. They could not believe that the Rebbe had given away the beautiful menorah.

"What's wrong? Do you think that one can fulfill the mitzvah of lighting a menorah only with a big, beautiful, silver menorah? You can fulfill your mitzvah just as well with my little Shalom Eliezer'l's menorah. That is just as beautiful in the eyes of the *Aibeshter*."

His son, Shalom Eliezer'l, was very young at the time but he never forgot the story. And he always made it a point to light with a simple menorah on at least one night of Chanukah, just to remind himself of his father's important lesson…

"You can fulfill your mitzvah just as well with my little Shalom Eliezer'l's menorah. That is just as beautiful in the eyes of the *Aibeshter*."

Absolutely Priceless

ith the month of April just around the corner, Chaim Turkelman, the business manager for a local yeshivah, knew that pretty soon he would receive the tuition check from the Lovitz family. When they received their tax refund each year, they always sent in as much as they could afford toward their children's tuition. Chaim tried to collect tuition from families without having to embarrass them or take way what they needed to live on. It was a hard and thankless job. Often, those who collect tuition are not the most well-liked people in the school, but everyone knew that Chaim did the best that he could.

When it came to the Lovitz family, though, it was hard to demand even the smallest amount of money. The family was poor. They were honest and fine, raising outstanding children, but there was no other way to say it. They were poor.

The children never received new clothing or toys, but there were some very valuable things that they did have — outstanding *derech eretz* and an understanding about what is right and what is wrong. So although the Lovitz' barely paid for their tuition, it was an honor to have such special children in the school.

That April, Chaim received a different message than usual — the Lovitz parents wanted to meet with him. He thought that perhaps, for this year, even the minimum tuition would be impossible, and prepared himself to tell them to give whatever they could afford. When they walked into Chaim's cluttered office and sat down, they immediately asked, "How much do we owe altogether for all the tuition breaks we have received over the past few years?" Chaim told them that they owed nothing, because if they had been given a break, they had deserved it. Therefore, there was no remaining balance. But the Lovitzes insisted on knowing, and so Chaim figured it out. The "breaks" amounted to nearly $35,000!

What happened next will forever change the way Chaim would look at sacrifice for a child's *chinuch*. Mr. Lovitz removed a large bag from under his coat and emptied it onto the desk. Chaim nearly fainted.

It was money. Tens. Twenties. Fifties. All smaller bills. Nothing over a fifty. An enormous pile of money was scattered across the desk. Chaim wanted to speak but had no idea what to say. Finally he just blurted out, "Where did you get all this money?"

Mr. Lovitz smiled proudly. After all the embarrassment and pain he had suffered from being the poorest man in town, he now afforded himself one proud smile. Then he explained. "Two weeks ago my wife went to a local silent auction. Although we could not afford much, my wife bought one ticket and placed it into a 'Split the Pot' box. She wrote on the back of the ticket that this money would be used for the tuition of our children." He smiled. "Chaim, we won … and now we are giving it all as our gift to the school to pay for our children's *s'char halimud*."

Chaim did not know what to say. "But … but … I can't accept it. I mean … did you ask your Rav what to do?"

"Chaim, we have no question as to what we should do with the money. In fact, let me tell you what we did last night." Chaim sat up, eager to hear the words that Mr. Lovitz spoke.

"Last night we gathered our children around the dining-room table." Chaim had been in their home and knew how poor their dining room looked. There wasn't much of a table, no two chairs matched, and their breakfront was nearly empty. Mr. Lovitz continued, "The children were curious as they knew that we wanted to show them something special. They waited for a big announcement. Finally we entered the room and I did exactly what I just did now. I poured the entire contents of the bag onto the table. You had to see the astonished looks on their faces. I explained that we had won the jackpot of $36,000. They were amazed by the money and wondered what we could possibly buy with all of it."

As Chaim listened, he had thoughts of his own — it could have gone toward so many things: new beds, toys, clothing, painting, carpeting, and many other things that a poor family needs. Mr. Lovitz continued his story. "I told the *kinderlach* what we had decided to do with the money. We were going to give it to their school, because we want them to know that their *chinuch* is worth more than anything else in the world to us. In the past we haven't been able to afford to pay in full … but now we will pay back what we owe."

Chaim wiped away his tears. His job was not always easy. Most of the time he had to bother people to give money. But for once he had met a special couple, who understood that the *chinuch* of their children … is absolutely priceless.

The Nicest One in the Store

The hustle and bustle of buying the nicest *lulav* and *esrog* were in full swing. Shloimy Chait, a well-known *mocheir* (seller), was busy with the constant flow of customers going in and out of his store. These were experts of the *lulav* and *esrog* shopping season. They knew exactly what they were looking for and were willing to pay top dollar for it. They wanted a "clean" esrog, one that had no *pintelach* (little dots) or *bletlach* (spots). Shloimy would walk into the back room where he kept his *esrogim* and search through the boxes to find the perfect one. When he walked back into the sales room he would hand the *esrog* over with such care that one would think he was handling a fancy jewel. Then the customers would look at the *esrog* to see if they could notice anything that might be wrong. Finally, when the buyer was sure that he had found the perfect *esrog* he was looking for, he would hand over up to $300 to pay for it and its equally beautiful *lulav*.

As Succos drew near, the supply of *esrogim* decreased, and Shloimy prepared to do what he always did — send his unsold *esrogim* to a market where they would be sold for much lower prices. People who were last-minute shoppers or were unable to afford the top-priced *esrogim* would be sure to find a bargain. As a precaution, each year when he shipped off the remaining *esrogim* he always held a few back, just in case someone in his neighborhood needed one for some reason just before Yom Tov.

The day before Succos, as he was about to take a short nap, there was a knock at the door. When he opened it he saw a little boy no older than 5 or 6, with beautiful brown eyes that shone with the excitement of the coming

Yom Tov. He was carrying a brown paper bag, holding it carefully with both hands. "Are you still selling *esrogim*? I would like to buy one."

Shloimy recognized the boy and knew that the family was quite poor. "How much do they cost?" the child asked.

Shloimy tried to keep the price as low as possible. "$15," he replied.

The boy looked up shyly and put his paper bag on the table. Out came nickels, dimes, and quarters that spread all over the table. He sat down and began to count. Shloimy did not know whether he should smile or cry. On the one hand, it was so sweet to see how serious this boy was about buying an *esrog* for himself. On the other hand, it was so sad because that the boy had probably spent much time and effort to gather enough money for this important purchase.

As the young boy finished counting he had come up with only a little more than half the required amount. "All I have is $7.90."

He looked down, disappointed and very sad.

Shloimy's heart nearly broke with pity for the child.

"Don't worry. You can have it for that price. Here."

Suddenly the boy's eyes lit up. "Really? Thank you so much!"

He ran out the door quickly, as he could hardly control his excitement. Jumping down the steps, he hurried down the block and as Shloimy watched he saw the boy present his *lulav* and *esrog* to a young man and then run back toward his own home just a few houses away.

Curious as to what had just happened, Shloimy immediately called the boy back and asked him, "Wasn't that *esrog* for you?"

"We don't have a lot of money in our house," explained the child, "but my father rewards us with coins every time we learn, to show us how much we should value learning Torah. Sometimes he gives us nickels, sometimes dimes, and every once in a while a quarter. Well, I decided that I wanted to save up the money I made from the learning in order to buy myself a *lulav* and *esrog* this year. But a few weeks ago my sister got married. When I asked my new brother-in-law where he was buying his *lulav* and *esrog*, he didn't really answer. I realized that he wouldn't be buying his own set because it was too expensive .... So I decided to give him mine .... I'm sorry. Did I do something wrong?"

Shloimy looked down into the boy's face and smiled.

He wondered if the young boy's brother-in-law knew that he had just received the nicest *esrog* in the entire store.

Or for that matter … any store.

A Tale of Two Buckets

man lived in a small village where no one had running water inside their homes. Like everyone else, every day he went to draw water from the well near the edge of the town – the opposite end of the town from where he lived. Every day he would draw two big bucketfulls and carry the containers home. In order to carry the buckets, he had to balance them on each end of a long wooden pole. However, there was a problem. One of the buckets was sound and none of its water leaked out, but the other bucket was cracked, and by the time he arrived home, only half of the water he had drawn was still in this bucket.

Now, the buckets in this story spoke to each other. The bucket that held onto its water — one could say that this bucket was quite "full of itself" — showed off to the other bucket, calling out to it, and asking it why it was always losing its contents. The broken bucket would answer explaining that he could not help it, he had tried to hold on but there were cracks inside that caused him to lose some of the water. He always tried as hard as he could to be proud, but he was ashamed of his failure and embarrassed in front of the other bucket. One day, however, all of that changed ….

The two buckets were hanging from either side of the pole when the snooty bucket called out to the other bucket, "Hey there, what is all that growing underneath you?"

The faulty bucket looked down and noticed that underneath him flowers and grass were growing. Under the snobby bucket, however, nothing was growing; there was just dry earth and stones. The haughty bucket wondered out loud why beautiful flowers were not growing beneath him as well.

The weaker bucket replied, "I have always felt hopeless next to you; my cracks and gaps caused half of my water to drip out. I just could not hold on to it. However, I see now that the water that leaked out has in fact not been wasted. It has dripped onto the dry earth day after day, year after year, and watered the ground below. Now there are beautiful flowers and grass beneath me."

Someone's Child

lthough they were a bit nervous about their trip to Eretz Yisrael, Moshe and Gila Apterfeld were excited as well. After all, they were taking their children to visit relatives, see the country, and visit gedolim. Above all else, Moshe and Gila were hoping to visit the *mekomos hakedoshim*, the holy places, where they could pour out their hearts in prayer.

It had been a few years since they had been to Israel and they were happy to be back. They spent some time davening Minchah at the *Kosel* and saying a few *kapitlach* of *Tehillim*. It felt wonderful to start off their visit in such a spiritually beautiful way. Returning to their apartment, they began planning the remainder of the trip. Some days would be set aside for meeting relatives, some days were selected for visits to *mekomos hakedoshim,* and, finally, they allowed time for touring and fun.

The family visited *Kever Rochel* and even *Me'aras HaMachpelah,* but Moshe did not feel anything special when he davened in these places. Perhaps on a different trip he would have spent another day and used it for davening there again, but he had to be fair to his kids, many of them little ones, and he kept his promise of reserving the last touring day for a trip to a water park in Kibbutz Chofetz Chaim. His kids were looking forward to some fun.

So off they went to enjoy their day at the water park. Surprisingly, this is where they would find the inspiration for which they had come to Eretz Yisroel. The children enjoyed their time going up and down the water slides on this beautiful warm summer day. The scene was picture-perfect — a family enjoying the refreshing waterslides, enjoying the day without a care in the world. After a few hours in the park, they went into the nearby picnic area to eat lunch and enjoy the beauty of the open area. Suddenly a loud noise intruded on the peaceful setting, as F-15 fighter jets flew overhead, whizzing by at high speed. The sight was awesome for one who had never seen it before

and certainly so for a young child. Moshe, as well as his children, looked up at the skies and watched in amazement.

As they watched, Gila noticed that just a few feet away from them a woman had burst into tears and was crying bitterly. Gila was not sure what she should do. At first she just stood by and hoped that just by standing next to her she would somehow soften the woman's pain. After a few moments had passed, Gila placed her hand gently on the woman's shoulder and held on to her, as if to say, "I am here for you if you need me."

Finally, she decided to talk to the woman and find out why the jets flying overhead had made her so upset. "Is someone you know flying in those fighter jets? Is it your husband? Your child?"

The last question seemed to have struck a chord. The woman, for the first time, looked up. She stopped crying for a moment, stared into Gila's eyes and answered, "No, it's not my child but it's someone's …."

Moshe watched the entire episode. The woman's words were so simple and yet so very powerful. It was true. In one moment it had become clear that every time a soldier — or for that matter anyone — is in pain, it is someone's child, someone's father, someone's mother. If we would realize this we would live differently. We would daven better and behave better and act nicer to each other.

Moshe and his family left Eretz Yisrael a few days later, with memories that would last a lifetime. They returned home with a whole new understanding about our fellow Jews and how we are all connected like family.

A child is not just a child; he or she is someone's child.

Someone who loves that child very much.

A Most Delicious Challah

hen Reb Meir'l of Premishlan and his followers arrived in the village, the townspeople gathered to greet them. They were taken to the home of Reb Shimon, an outstanding *baal tzedakah,* to whom so many turned in their times of need. It was almost time for Shabbos, and all hurried to make preparations.

With the important visitor in town, that Friday evening the atmosphere in the shul was one of excitement. The townspeople showed up a little earlier than usual, as they all wanted to make sure to hear and appreciate the Rebbe's davening.

After leading the congregation in the *Kabbalas Shabbos* and Maariv *tefillos* and wishing the townspeople "*Gut Shabbos,*" Reb Meir walked back to the home of Reb Shimon to begin a most memorable Shabbos meal. While the *zemiros* were beautiful and the words of Torah were quite meaningful, surprisingly, it was the food which would leave its mark on Reb Meir and the others.

After Kiddush, Reb Meir recited the *Hamotzi* and tasted the challah. But this was not ordinary challah! There was something unique about it — Reb Meir declared that the challah had the taste of Gan Eden! Surprised that in an ordinary home he would experience the taste of Gan Eden, Reb Meir asked his host who had made the challah. Reb Shimon proudly answered that his wife had, and Reb Meir asked if he could be told the special ingredient that had been added to this incredible challah.

However, when Reb Shimon asked his wife, she said that in fact she had not baked the challah that week. An orphan girl had knocked on the door earlier that day and had asked if she could help out around the house in order to earn some money. Eager to help the *yesomah,* Reb Shimon's wife had offered her the opportunity to make the challah.

The search for the special ingredient continued. They called in the young girl — who was only 11 years old — and asked her, but she replied that she had not added any unusual ingredients. Curious to get to the bottom of the mystery, Reb Meir thought of asking the question another way – not about the ingredients, but about *how* she had made the challah. Surprised and shy, she explained that as she formed the challah she remembered her mother rolling out matzah dough.

Reb Meir smiled as the girl said her mother would roll the pin and sing the mellow tunes of *Hallel,* as is the custom. The girl stopped as she thought for a moment about her mother, who had passed away not long before. Again Reb Meir carefully pressed on, asking what else might have happened as she made the challah.

The little girl shyly added that while she sang the songs of *Hallel* she remembered her mother saying that she couldn't help but cry as she rolled out the matzos. The child went on to say that she cried softly too as she braided the challah. The crowd watched as Reb Meir smiled, thanked the girl, and wished her well. He now looked around at the crowd, convinced that he had discovered the secret magical ingredient.

"This is why the challah had the taste of Gan Eden. Life is not simple and for as many moments of happiness that we enjoy, there always seem to be even more times of pain. But when a young girl can change her tears into the song of *Hallel,* then we have experienced the *taam* of Gan Eden."

A Beautiful Present

The last-minute packing was hectic as usual. Baruch Fried, a fifth-grade rebbi in the Torah School of Greater Washington, was preparing to head off to spend the second days of Pesach with his in-laws. His wife, Leah, was from Paramus, New Jersey, and the ride up there would take between three and four hours, depending on traffic. After loading the last few items into the car, they drove away.

Typically, Sunday is not a great day for traveling. But that day traffic would be even heavier than usual because it was a non-Jewish holiday, one of the busiest travel days of the year. Surprisingly, however, the trip was uneventful and they reached Paramus a few hours before Yom Tov. It was then that Aviva suddenly realized that she had forgotten a very important item — her children's medicine.

The two Fried boys had an unusual condition (there an only about 80 such cases in the United States) and could not eat normally unless they took their medicine. This medication is not something pharmacies stocked regularly, so the Frieds knew it would be difficult to find it in the area and begin frantically calling every pharmacy around. Having no success, they figured they'd better decide soon if they would have to drive back home to get the medication.

Finally, after many phone calls and getting some useful information, they decided to call their friend in New Square, Shmuel Zalmanowitz, a kind chassidishe *Yid,* who they knew was involved with a family member with the same condition and would have the medication. Shmuel immediately offered to share his medication with them and they were delighted. But, unfortu-

nately, they now realized that it was too late to drive to New Square and then back to Paramus. Shmuel suggested that they meet at a place somewhere between the two locations. Each would then probably have enough time to make it home in time for Yom Tov. Hard as it was for the Frieds to trouble this kind man and possibly prevent him from getting home in time for Yom Tov, they knew they had no choice. So they set out to meet him.

When they reached the meeting place — the parking lot of the Pathmark supermarket in Monsey — it was less than an hour before Yom Tov. They were pleasantly surprised to see that the fellow was standing outside his car waiting for them! On the hood of his station wagon was a lot of delicious *Pesachdig* chocolate, and a new copy of *Spirit* magazine; not only had he brought the medication, but he also brought all the necessary supplies (syringes, gauze pads, and alcohol swabs) even though Baruch had told him that he had these items. It was all wrapped up beautifully with a stuffed animal on the side. This was too much to believe! Baruch and his friend Shmuel greeted each other warmly, and Baruch thanked Shmuel for all of his kindness. Baruch then went back to his car and gave the medicine to each of his children.

Realizing that he had less than 45 minutes left before Yom Tov, Baruch was about to begin the ride to his in-laws' home when one of Shmuel's boys ran up to the door of his car. In his hands was a yellow toy school bus.

"What's this for?" Baruch asked, completely surprised.

"It's for your children. I want them to have it." The young boy, dressed in his Yom Tov finest, had the look of a little angel.

Although Baruch was very moved by the child's present, he felt that he could not accept the gift and insisted that the boy keep it for himself. But Shmuel wouldn't hear of it and after much convincing, Baruch finally agreed to keep the present. He had a hunch, though, that the toy had belonged to one of Shmuel's children, and that he had convinced his son to give the toy away to Baruch's children. By now it was really getting very close to sunset and Baruch could no longer argue the point.

As he was about to pull away he noticed that the other little boy in Shmuel's car was crying. Baruch now realized he was right. *They must have taken the toy away from this child,* he thought. Baruch felt terrible and decided that he would not allow himself or his children to be the cause of another child's unhappiness. He was most certainly not going to keep the toy. His children probably would not even appreciate it as much as Shmuel's boys would.

Very quickly, he walked to Shmuel's car. "Please take it back. I see that the little child is crying."

Shmuel smiled at Baruch and began to explain. "My 4-year-old is not crying because someone took away his present. It's just the opposite. He's crying because he *also* wants to give your children a present!" Baruch shook his head, smiled in disbelief, and wiped tears from his eyes.

"By the way," Shmuel called out, "I just want you to know that these are their very own *afikoman* presents. They just received them and they wanted your children to have them. They knew it would make them a little bit happier."

Baruch and his wife knew that the road to raising their children would have many challenges. But their job was made just a little bit easier by a father and two young children with very big hearts.

Glossary

Aibeshter: (Yiddish) literally, the One Above; G-d

ba'al tzedakah: one who gives large amounts of charity

chasan: a bridegroom

cheder: elementary school

chinuch: education

daven: (Yiddish) to pray

davening: (Yiddish) praying; prayers collectively

derech eretz: courtesy; manners

esrog (esrogim): citron, one of the four species taken on Succos

gadol (pl. gedolim): one who is great in Torah learning

Gut Shabbos: (Yiddish) good Shabbos

Hallel: a song of praise to G-d, part of the Rosh Chodesh and holiday services

Hamotzei: the blessing said over bread

kallah: a bride

kapitlach: verses

kehillah: community; congregation

Kever Rochel: the gravesite of the Matriarch Rachel

kinderlach: (Yiddish) children

kitel: the shroud-like garment worn on certain solemn occasions

kibud av v'eim: the commandment to honor one's parents

Kol Nidrei: the prayer that begins the Yom Kippur service

lulav: palm branch, one of the four species taken on Succos

Me'aras Hamachpelah: the gravesite of the Patriarchs and Matriarchs

melamed: a teacher

nadan: a dowry

neshamah: the soul

Pesachdig: kosher for Passover

rabbosai: gentlemen

s'char limud: tuition

shiur: lecture; lesson

shtiebel: literally, room; a small *shul,* usually used by Chassidim

shul: a synagogue

taam: taste; flavor

talmid chacham: a learned person; a Torah scholar

tefillos: prayers

Tehillim: Psalms

veshinantam levanecha: "and you should teach it to your sons."
    (*Devarim,* 6:7)

yesomah: (feminine form) orphan

Yid: (Yiddish) Jew

Yiddishe maidel: (Yiddish) a Jewish girl

zechusim: merits